SECOND SERIES OF
GRADED PIANOFORTE STUDIES

GRADE 3

THE ASSOCIATED BOARD OF
THE ROYAL SCHOOLS OF MUSIC

SECOND SERIES
GRADED PIANOFORTE STUDIES
GRADE 3

Broken chords, and freedom of the wrist

LE COUPPEY, Op.20 No.18

A.B. 776

Evenness in two-part playing

KÖHLER, Op.249 No.170

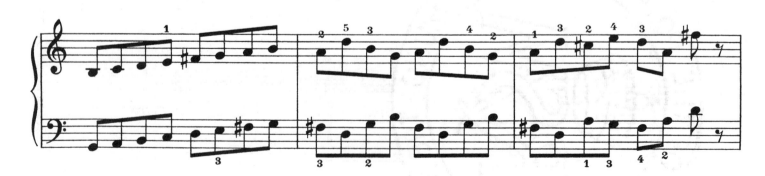

Two-part playing and rhythm

STAMATY

Right-hand scale passages

BERTINI, Op. 100 No. 1

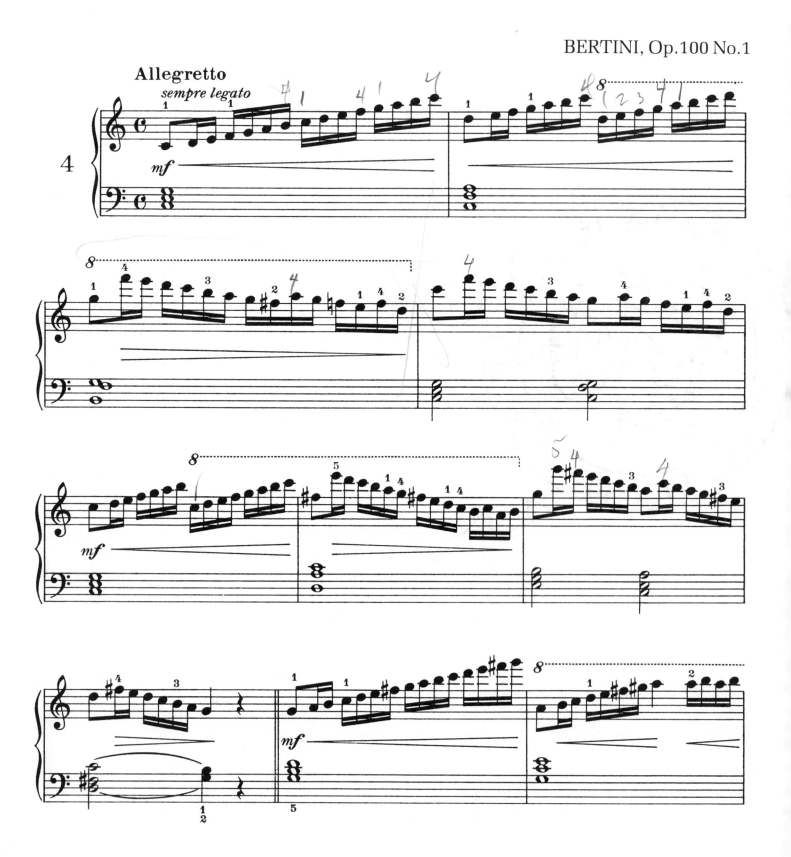

Agility in scale passages and leaps

BERENS, Op.61 No.2

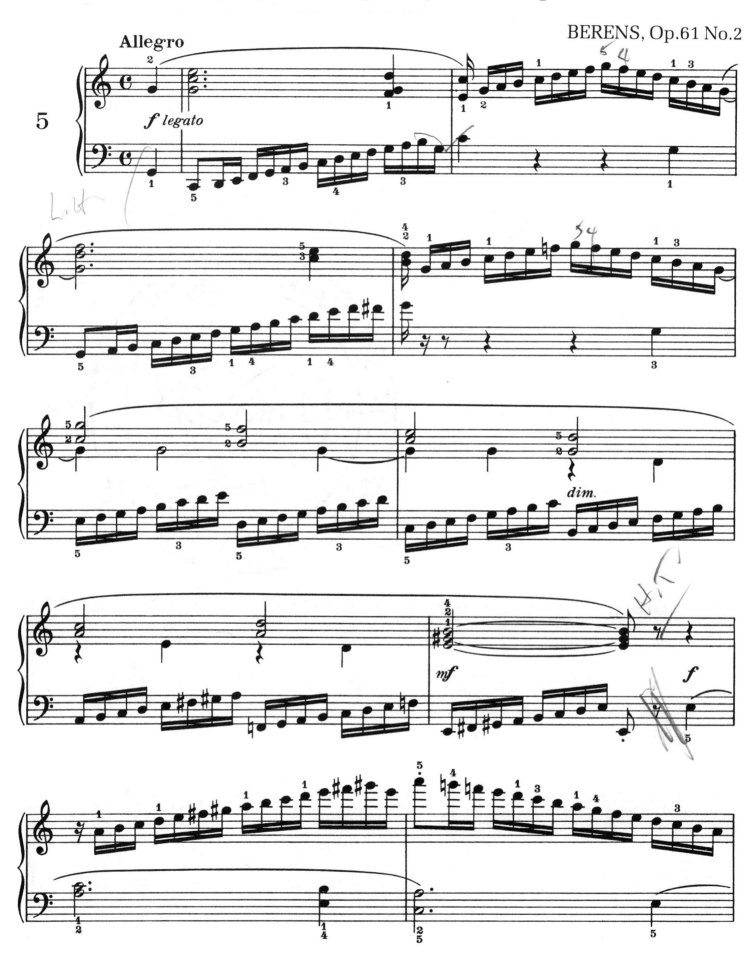

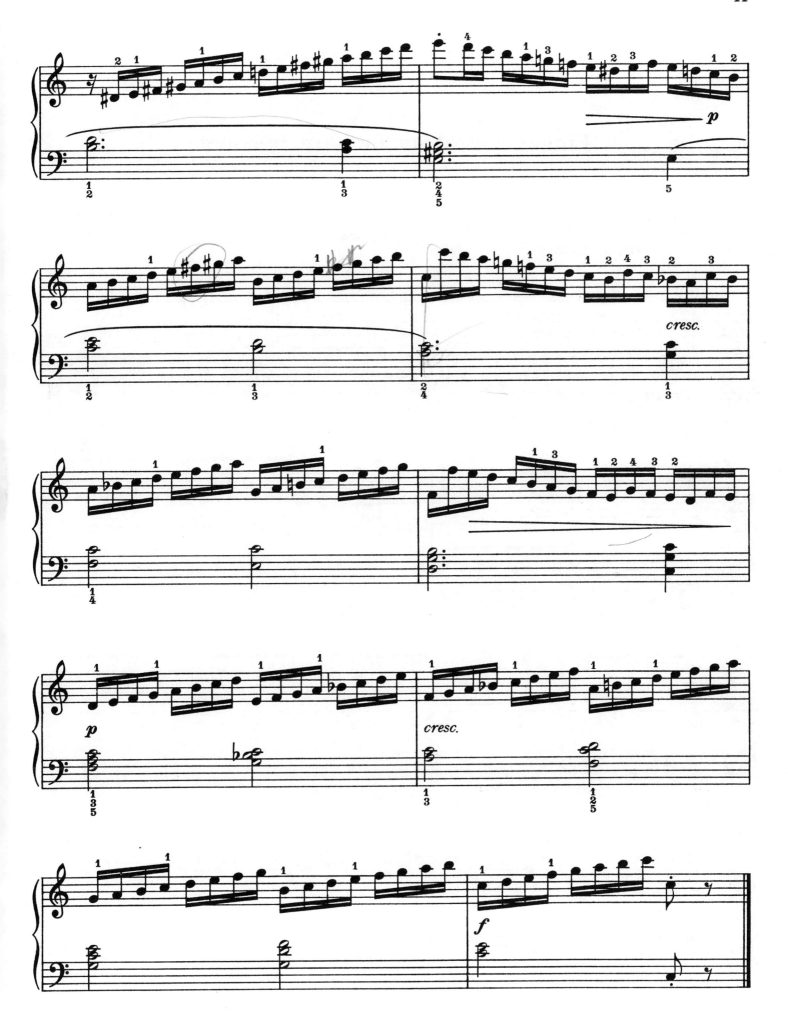

Finger control and fore-arm freedom

GURLITT, Op.50 No.7

Double notes in both hands

STAMATY

Legato passages between the hands

DUNHILL, Op.74/II No.2

Broken chords and staccato

CZERNY, Op.139 No.71

Broken chords in both hands

KÖHLER, Op.256 No.13

Skips in both hands

BERTINI

11

Independence of hands in staccato

KIRCHNER

12

Independence of the hands

GURLITT, Op.50 No.17

Rhythm and clarity in repeated notes

CZERNY, Op.261 No.22

Agility and accentuation

Con moto, scherzando

HELLER, Op.125 No.7

Quiet chords with left hand crossing over

GURLITT

Phrasing and two-part playing

KIRCHNER, Op.71 No.26

For evenness and speed

LOESCHHORN, Op.65 No.46